THE

Quest

—— [BOOK TWO] ——

COACHING
FOR JESUS
IN A BOTTOM-LINE WORLD

A 10-LESSON STUDY ON BECOMING
A LEGACY BUILDER FOR GOD'S KINGDOM

Romans 12:2

R O D   O L S O N

D E D I C A T I O N

I wish to dedicate this book to the Master
Coach and architect of my life, my Lord and
Savior Jesus Christ. The principles he left us are
truly timeless and life changing. I would also
like to thank my wife, Marla for all her patience
and love as a coach's wife and mother. This
book would not have been possible if not for
the vision of Frosty Westering, the ministry of
Scotty Kessler and Wes Neal, the steadfastness
of Kirk Talley and the unselfishness of Johnny
Square. I would also like to thank Derek
Fullmer and the Colorado FCA staff for all their
prayers and support. Finally, I want to thank
the Air Force football staff for their inspiration
and all the coaches and their spouses that we
have known over the years...this is for you.

Legacy Builders Book Two

Rod Olson

ISBN 1-929478-77-1

Cross Training Publishing
P.O. Box 1874
Kearney, NE 68847
(800) 430-8588

Copyright © 2006 by Cross Training Publishing

This book is manufactured in the United States of America.

Library of Congress Cataloging in Publication Data in Progress.

CONTENTS

GROUP COVENANT

I, _____

Commit with my Legacy Builders group to do the following:

1. Complete the Legacy Builder worksheet each week before the group session.
2. Pray regularly for my fellow group members.
3. Participate in all group sessions unless urgent circumstances beyond my control prevent my attendance.
4. Participate openly and honestly in the group sessions.
5. Keep confidential any personal matters shared by others in the group.
6. Be patient and compassionate with my fellow Christian coaches and my school as we grow closer to God and see how He wants us to serve.
7. I will pray for my school, my staff and my players at least one time per week.

OTHERS YOU WILL BE COMMITTING TO PRAY FOR:

_____

_____

_____

Signed:_____

Date:_____

LEGACY BUILDER GROUP MEMBERS:

_____

_____

_____

_____

_____

_____

INTRODUCTION

WHAT'S IN YOUR BOX?

Repeat this study from Book One if your group
hasn't already completed it.

*"What is the No. 1, central motivating
factor in your life?"*

READ: Colossians 3:23-25

I. WHAT IS DRIVING YOU?

In his book Half-Time, Bob Buford is a CEO trying to decide what to do with
the second half of his life. To help him discern what to do, he hires a strategic
planning consultant that asks him to write down the No. 1 priority or central
motivating factor in his life from which all his secondary loyalties derive their
meaning or place of importance in his life. He then told him to put it in a box
that was placed on the table. Lastly, he informed the CEO that this one loyalty
will be the foundation of his life and it will affect all other areas of his
life…good or bad.

***What is (not what you wish it was) the No. 1, central motivating
factor or loyalty in your life?***

 EXTRA POINT: If you are having trouble narrowing your loyalties
down to one, remember that Jesus tells us that no one can serve two
masters, for if he/she does, they will hate the one and love the other.
(see Matthew 6:24) Find a way to get it down to one.

II. THE FILTER

The water filter in your refrigerator is designed to catch and keep all the impurities out of your drinking water. Like it or not, the No. 1 loyalty that you listed above is your filter for life. If the loyalty you listed was finances, then all the decisions you will make in your life will be based upon how those decisions will help you (directly or indirectly) save or make money. If your loyalty was your family, than all your major decisions will be based on how it affects your family and so on. Wouldn't you want a filter that protects you and keeps you safe, while still providing the nutrients you need? Jesus wants to be the filter that protects you from harm and directs your life.

What do you use as your filter when making decisions?
As a coach have you considered letting a relationship with Jesus be the No. 1 central motivating factor in your life? What would that look like?

Read aloud Jeremiah 29:11-13, How does this verse apply to you?

III. "HEY COACH! THIS IS THE 1ST DAY OF THE REST OF YOUR LIFE!"

God has given us all the power to choose what we want to put in our box! You have the power to choose to put Jesus Christ as the only thing in your box so He can be the foundation that will affect all areas of your life!

HOW TO TAKE ACTION:
1) What do I want to be remembered for?
2) What kind of Legacy do I want to leave behind?
3) Do I have a Destiny to fulfill?

*If you don't like what is in your box and want to put Jesus first in your life, or you do not have a personal relationship with Jesus Christ, please pray this short prayer and tell someone you did. "Lord Jesus, I need you! I want you to be the #1 loyalty in my life. Thank you for dying on the cross for me. Forgive me and cleanse me from my sins. I trust you as my Lord and Savior. Help me to be the person you created me to be. In Jesus' name. Amen.

MEMORIZE: Matthew 6:33

But seek first his kingdom and his righteousness, and all these things will be given to you as well.

| WEEK I |

THE QUEST

"Where you've been, where you are, and where God has you going"

Read: Romans 12:1-2

I. QUEST: A JOURNEY IN SEARCH OF ADVENTURE

We are all on a journey…the journey of life and I have yet to meet an athlete that doesn't have a unique personal history. Some individuals have had more trials than others but everyone has a story to tell. God wants to use your past experiences (good and bad) and present situations to further His kingdom in the future. That is the Quest or journey that we are on for Christ. Regardless of our past failures God _____ us and uses us for His glory. But before we can embark on a journey we must ask ourselves three questions:

Where do I come from?
Why am I here?
Where am I going?

EXTRA POINT: If the apostle Paul were coaching you, how would you apply his teaching on 'be transformed by the renewing of your mind'?

II. THE PAST

Many people blame the past for their present problems, but God sees the past differently. By utilizing our past experiences God _____ us for ministering to others in need.

Are you willing for your past to be known to others if it helps them to know God? Why or why not?

III. The Present (Read Philippians 2:13)

As coaches, we have a hard time letting go of losses. We waste time beating ourselves up thinking about what we could have done differently to avoid the mistakes that caused defeat. As Christians, we too waste a great deal of time holding on to past mistakes and wrong doings. But just as we must learn from our mistakes, we must move on from losses to have a chance to be successful in the future. As Christians we must learn from our mistakes and let go of the past sins we have _____ so that we may be of use to God in the future.

What do rebellion, robbery, hatred, deceit, adultery and murder have to do with Moses, David, Paul, Abraham, and Jacob?

Did God use these people in a mighty way? Why?

HOW TO TAKE ACTION:
To insure that you learn from your mistakes and to be well equipped for the future teach yourself and your athletes to do three Things when you/they make a mistake:

1) Admit it!
2) Fix it!
3) Forget it & Don't repeat it!

MEMORIZE: Ephesians 2:10

For we are God's workmanship, created in Christ Jesus to do good works, which God prepared in advance for us to do.

Answer Key: 1. accepts 2. equips 3. confessed

THE CLIMB

"Stepping Stones or Spiritual Landmarks?"

READ: Romans 8:28-33

I. PREDESTINED...

As coaches, it seems as though we are always trying to direct the paths of our careers. Isn't it good to know, that in all things God works for the good of those who love Him and who have been called according to His purpose? That means that everywhere you have been and all the experiences you have had are part of a master game plan that God has designed for you. Our goal as Christian-coaches needs to be seeking God's _____ in all things and make our decisions based upon His will!

As you look back on your coaching career, describe a situation where you know God was involved: (Example: maybe you didn't get a job and it turned out to be a blessing)

II. MY WILL VS. GOD'S WILL (READ MATTHEW 6:9-11)

Whether we are making career decisions or daily decisions God has given us the ability to make choices. As a Christian-coach our choices are not usually between good and bad, but between good and better. If we are to make God- pleasing decisions we must start by choosing God's _____ over ours. We must make sure we do this at the beginning of the decision process not at the end. (Example: "Lord whatever your will is here I commit to it now."- *not*, "Lord, your will be done as long as it is the same as mine.")

Describe a situation where you had to choose between good and better, how did you come to a decision and did you put God's will first?

III. SPIRITUAL LANDMARKS

As coaches we often look back at past games or experiences with opponents to get an idea of what might happen in an upcoming game. God uses a similar method for helping us determine how He is working in our lives by giving us _____ landmarks. These landmarks show a specific time when we know that God has guided us.

 EXTRA POINT: : On a separate sheet of paper make a list of your Spiritual landmarks from as far back as possible and see things from God's point of view.

HOW TO TAKE ACTION:

1) Seek God's Will first, in prayer and His word.
2) Look at your spiritual landmark list to help you see things from God's viewpoint
3) Choose the option that is most consistent with what God has been doing in your life…if things are still not clear, pray and continue to wait for His guidance.
4) To 'wait' means to tarry or be doing something while waiting. Use this time of waiting to love others more than yourself and to seek God with all your heart.

MEMORIZE: Psalm 27:14

Wait for the Lord; be strong and take heart and wait for the Lord.

Answer Key: 1. viewpoint   2. will   3. spiritual

| WEEK 3 |

BE TO DO...
NOT DO TO BE!
"God wants a changed heart...not blind obedience"

READ: I Corinthians 15:7-10, Luke 10:38-42

I. THE GRINDER

As an athlete, you were taught that a great work ethic could overcome many obstacles and shortcomings. As coaches, we have taken that work ethic to another level and discovered that if we work harder and grind at the office longer, we can gain an advantage for our team and perhaps a win. But as we grow in our faith and long to be closer to God, we sometimes try so hard to do so many things in attempt to get closer to God, we lose the true meaning of the grace that Paul talks about in Corinthians. God wants us to have a _____ heart and enjoy _____ with Him daily. He doesn't want a coach that is trying to work his/her way into (God's) grace.

What would it mean to you if God said, "My child, be to do-don't do to be"?
(Ex: God is encouraging me to remember I can't work my way into a relationship with Him)

Do you have balance in your life physically, emotionally, socially and spiritually? What does balance or margin in each of those areas look like?

II. BE TRANSFORMED - INTEGRATE JESUS INTO EVERYTHING!
REPUTATION VS. CHARACTER...BE RELATIONSHIP ORIENTED RATHER THAN TASK ORIENTED!

John Wooden once said, "Your *reputation* is other people's perception of you and *character* is what you are." Your reputation is developed by your actions while your character is developed by the power and _____ of God working in your heart.

As you grow in your faith what type of person/coach do you sense God is asking you to be? How can you allow God to help you become that person/coach?

 EXTRA POINT:
"Your Character determines what you can be trusted with!" -Blackaby

---

III. RESTING IN GOD…HARD WORK! (READ LUKE 10:38-42)
Are you a Mary or a Martha?

We tell our players that if their 'heart isn't in it' we will be able to tell by their outward actions. As coaches, we don't want robots, we want players motivated from the heart. If we hope to enjoy God's presence in our lives and move closer to Him, we must work hard to maintain a _____ between our outward actions and the true intentions God has put in our hearts. We must start from the heart, which directs the mind, which controls our actions. Now that is something worth working for!
How can the Holy Spirit help you in the fight to 'rest in God' and align your actions with God's will? How can you pray more and do less?

HOW TO TAKE ACTION:
1) Ask God to show you the type of character He wants you to possess.
2) Ask God to reveal any offensive way in you so that you may confess.
3) Pray for a pure heart and clean hands daily and enjoy God.
4) Instead of operating your schedule at 120% see if you can operate it at an 80% capacity so you can have 20% available to be led by God.

MEMORIZE: Psalm 139:23-24

Search me, O God, and know my heart; test me and know my anxious thoughts. See if there is any offensive way in me, and lead me in the way everlasting.

Answer Key: 1. changed 2. being 3. grace 4. consistency

| WEEK 4 |

MATURITY THROUGH ADVERSITY!

"Everyone wants to go to heaven but no one wants to die!"

READ: James 1:1-8

I. "NO PAIN...NO GAIN!"

As coaches, it seems as though another crisis or trial is always around the corner. Often, we see a crisis as a threat or tragedy, however God would like us to see our trials as _____ points not breaking points. Even James, the brother of Jesus knew how tough life could be, therefore he encourages us to see _____ in our trials because they are the vehicle God uses to make us mature and _____ for His kingdom building! If we want to be complete in our development as a Christian-coach we must understand that God is going to use tough times to develop the character He wants in us.

Do 'tough times' frighten you or point you toward God? Why?

II. DISTRACTION VS. OPPORTUNITY (READ 2 CORINTHIANS 5:7)

As Christian-coaches we are constantly on the lookout for teachable moments for our athletes, but what about ourselves? We often make the mistake of seeing a crisis as a distraction rather than an **opportunity** to grow closer to God. As Paul writes in Corinthians, we must live by faith and not by sight. We must see our trials as opportunities for growth.

How can you help yourself see God more on a daily basis?
What are some ways you can help yourself to view a crisis as an
opportunity for growth and not a distraction?

EXTRA POINT: "Pain can be a good thing as it has the ability to force us to focus our attention on the important things at hand!"
- General O. Sampson, US Air Force

III. GOD'S WAY OR MY WAY?

In the midst of every trial or crisis, we have to make a choice as to whether we follow our own instincts or seek God's guidance and do it His way. Remember, God uses trials and difficult situations to draw us closer to Him.

Think of some recent trials you have had to endure. Did you go
with your own instincts or seek the Lord in it? Why or why not?

 COACHES CHALLENGE: As you deal with difficult situations, ask yourself what is God doing and how can I use this to help myself or someone else grow closer to God?

How to see trials as Growing points and not breaking points:
1) Don't be so focused on the crisis that you are unable to see God in it.
2) Remember that God will use trials to strengthen your character and to make you more useful for His kingdom building.
3) Prior to deciding how you will handle the situation, ask yourself, "Am I going to handle this my way or God's way?"
4) Pray for guidance and that you will stand firm in your faith to honor God and to grow closer to Him.

MEMORIZE: Isaiah 7:9

If you do not stand firm in your faith, you will not stand at all.

Answer Key: 1. growing 2. joy 3. useful 4. opportunity

SELF-SERVING LEADER TO SERVANT-LEADER

"With God it's all about people not productivity!"

READ: Matthew 20:25-28

I. WORLD THINKING VS. BIBLICAL TRUTHS?

If you have ever been a head coach you are aware of how fine a line it is between taking care of your own needs and helping others meet theirs. It isn't very difficult to follow the world's thinking and just look out for #1. As we read in Matthew, even the disciples were influenced by the world's thinking as they argued about who will sit at the right and left of Jesus when he comes into his kingdom. But, Jesus reminds us and the disciples that the only way to achieve a place of honor in God's kingdom is through useful _____ to God and others, not self-importance, ambition or respect.

How much have you let the world's thinking influence your own thinking? Why? How can you coach & live from a Biblical viewpoint in a win at all costs world?

II. BE 'RUTHLESS' WITH YOUR TIME NOT WITH PEOPLE!

Tony Dungy, head coach of the Indianapolis Colts, is described as a players' coach. Meaning, his players enjoy playing for him because he makes it clear that they are more important to him than himself or his schedule. We must make time for our players and families, our daytimers and schedules cannot be more important than the people God has entrusted us with. Also, If I want to know what kind of a coach you are, I won't ask your 1st or 2nd teamers, I will ask your 3rd stringers and managers...what type of answers will I get?

Remember "Happy players play Better!"
Are your family/players getting the main course or the 'left overs' from you? What can you do to insure they are getting the 'main course' of you?

 EXTRA POINT: "All the kings and queens I have known in history sent their people out to die for them. I know only one King who decided to die for His people. I will follow that leader!"- Chuck Colson

---

III. DIE TO YOURSELF AND LIVE FOR CHRIST! (READ ROM. 6:11-14)

If we wish to be true servant leaders we must die to ourselves, in other words we must not live for our own gain but for Christ our King. Being a servant leader is a _____ with eternal significance. Once you commit to being a servant leader you will never return to your 'old self'...you are a new creation!

How do you teach your players to put aside their selfish needs?
How can you 'die to yourself' on a daily basis and live for Jesus Christ?

A SERVANT-LEADER'S TOOL BOX CHECKLIST
❏ A personal mission statement that is easy to understand and remember.
❏ A personal definition of success that God would approve.
❏ A set of priorities to help you be ruthless with your time and not people.
❏ At least 1-2 accountability partners to keep you on the right track.
❏ A journal to record triumphs, challenges and lessons you have learned.
❏ A well used Bible for daily living and growing.
❏ A daily dose of solitude, prayer, and study of scripture and exercise.
❏ A memorized set of scriptures that allow you to fight the daily fight!
❏ Understand that you and your players are "men and women built for others!"

MEMORIZE: I Corinthians 10:24

No one should seek his own good, but the good of others.

Answer Key: 1. service 2. lifestyle

DEFEATING THE ENEMY

"Basic battle tactics for freedom in Christ!"

READ: Peter 5:7-9, Hebrews 12:6-11

I. "WHATEVER DOESN'T KILL YOU MAKES YOU STRONGER"

I think nearly 7 out of 10 weight rooms or locker rooms have that slogan on the wall somewhere. As coaches, we know that our job is to take an athlete to a level that he/she cannot get to by themselves. We motivate them by telling them to do the little things right every day, strip themselves of anything that may hinder their development, and stay focused on their long-term goals. At times, our players may even require discipline. We discipline our players in hopes of getting them and keeping them on the right track. As we see in the passage above in Hebrews, discipline is not enjoyable at the time but it does produce a harvest of _____ and _____ for those who have been trained by it.

If we trust that God is our loving Father, how should that affect our view of how God disciplines us?

EXTRA POINT: Through discipline, God is bringing us back to a relationship with Him, when Satan attacks; he is attempting to put distance between us and God!

II. THE BATTLE IN THE COURTROOM OF GOD (READ EPHESIANS 6:12)

Everyday in the spiritual realm, there is a battle going on in the courtroom of God. Satan is the prosecutor that is looking to condemn each one of us for our sins. God is the judge and Jesus Christ is defending us…the accused. As the prosecutor, Satan, attempts to show the court that we are not worthy of heaven or freedom by stating all of our sins against God. Our lawyer (Jesus) objects and states that those accusations are not relevant as the defendant (us) has confessed those sins to the court and has been forgiven and is no longer bound to the wrong doings. Jesus then tells the court that this case against us should be dropped, as the penalty has been paid in full by His death. The judge (God) agrees with Jesus and we are set free from the wrong doings and Satan's accusations. As we view our freedom from sin in a courtroom drama, we see how important it is that we confess _____ our sins to Jesus Christ and repent, so he, as our lawyer, can go before the judge and speak on our behalf. We must remember that in the spiritual realm, the enemy is constantly taking us to court and putting us on the stand, so it is imperative that we are in a constant state of confession and repentance each day with Jesus Christ, as we know we are going to continue to sin as we are fallen human beings. *Why is it important to confess our sin?*

III. THE 6 R's OF FORGIVENESS & FREEDOM IN JESUS CHRIST

When looking to break free of past sins or to remove things that the enemy looks to accuse you of in the courtroom of God you can remember and pray the 6 R's in order:

Repentance - Confess and Repent of your sins to God (Acts 3:19, 1 John 1:9)

Renounce - Declare that the influence of past sins confessed is gone (Philippians 3:13)

Resist/Reject - Declare that you will not succumb to the same sin in the future. (James 4:7, Eph. 4:27)

Rebuke - With the authority and humility of Jesus Christ verbally shut down Satan and his doings. (Matt. 17:18, Jude 1:9)

Replace - Replace the lies and fears of Satan with the Truth and Promises of God through the name of Jesus Christ, the Blood of Jesus Christ, and the Victory (resurrection) of the cross. (Romans 12:2, 2 Peter 1:4)

Rely - Rely on the word of God and the power of the Scriptures. (Matthew 4:4)

MEMORIZE: Ephesians 6:12

For our struggle is not against flesh and blood… but against the rulers of this dark world and against the spiritual forces of evil in the heavenly realms.

Answer Key: 1. righteousness 2. peace 3. all

EASY TO PLEASE BUT HARD TO SATISFY

"God will put you in tough situations to show you how to serve Him"

Read: 2 Timothy 2:1-7

I. PREPARING FOR ADVERSITY

A great high school coach would prepare his players for adversity by assuring them that they can only control two things in sport; their _____ and their _____. Everything else is out of their control. This same coach made it clear that there will be hard times ahead and that he will demand perfection, but if they come to every practice/game with a great attitude and an unparalleled work ethic, he will be more than pleased. We see the same approach from Paul as he wrote in the above passage to Timothy. Paul taught that we would face hardship, but that we should endure struggles as a good _____ of Christ, meaning that we should maintain our discipline and keep a good attitude as we strive for victory!

As a coach on God's team what do you think are the only 2 things God is asking of you on a daily basis? How can you model that to your family and players?

 EXTRA POINT: Great players make big plays in big games! Do you thrive under pressure or do you just try to survive under pressure?

II. THE PRESSURE COOKER (READ 1 CORINTHIANS 10:12-13)

We all have felt the pressure of a big game. Lou Holtz had a unique way of relieving the pressure his players were feeling before big games. Coach

Holtz would tell his players that the definition of 'pressure' is being asked to do something that they are not prepared to do. Therefore, they need not feel pressured because they have been_____ for today's game and all situations. As the Master Coach, God has prepared us for every tough situation that lies ahead and just as players must be put in a pressure packed game to test what they have learned, we too, are tested in the game of life as God allows us to be put in difficult situations. These tests occur so that we can continue to grow in our relationship with Him and become stronger in our faith.

What is your definition of pressure and how has God has prepared you for tough situations?

III. GOD IS THE PERFECT COACH AS HE IS…EASY TO PLEASE BUT HARD TO SATISFY!

As coaches, we would love to have a reputation of being easy to please but hard to satisfy. As we serve our God, we know He has a reputation of being easy to please but hard to satisfy. In other words, God is _____ as we make strides toward becoming more like Jesus Christ everyday; However, He makes it clear that we are not to be satisfied with mediocrity and that He wants us to strive for _____ daily.

How can you be a coach that is 'easy to please but hard to satisfy' for your players? How can you be a person that is 'easy to please but hard to satisfy' for your family?

How You can Thrive under Pressure:
1) Maintain a great attitude and effort in your relationship with God.
2) Spiritual discipline, (i.e., quiet time, reading scripture, prayer, journaling.)
3) See difficult situations as 'prime time games' that you are prepared for.
4) Focus on the Cross

MEMORIZE: John 16:33

I have told you these things, so that in me you may have peace. In this world you will have trouble. But take heart! I have overcome the world.

Answer Key: 1. attitude 2. effort 3. soldier 4. prepared 5. pleased 6. perfection

WEEK 8

COACHING &
LIVING 'ON THE EDGE'

"Gain the edge of living daily with Christ…
the entrance to the Zone"

READ: Colossians 2: 6-15, Matthew 5:5

I. SUBMITTING TO CHRIST FOR STRENGTH

One of the biggest fears I had prior to submitting to coach with Biblical principles was my fear of becoming soft and weak as a coach. I feared that in the world's eyes I would be seen as a coach that had lost his competitive edge. However, Paul reminds us in Colossians that we _____ our strength from Christ, the most powerful name in Heaven and on earth! To be weak means to have an absence of power, while meekness is defined as bridled power. When the world says we are weak and worthless because we coach for an eternal significance, Christ sees us as meek, strong and determined. When the world thinks we don't care about winning and we just want our players to 'try hard', Christ knows we are demanding perfection and striving for the prize to bring Him glory. If Christ is our _____, we are free from the world's thinking and judgements.

As a Christian-coach do you see yourself as a meek or a weak coach/competitor? Why? How can you be more of a meek coach and let Jesus guide you to coach for an eternal significance?

II. THE THREE SIDED COIN…ANOTHER WAY TO COACH

Many people think that a coin has only two sides. However, if you look at the coin sideways you will notice a third side… the Edge. As we look for ways to motivate ourselves (and those we influence) to live a transformed life in Jesus Christ, we must look to live on the _____. We must tap into the supernatural power of the Holy Spirit and gain the edge of living daily with Jesus Christ as our source of strength and inspiration. If we listen to the world for inspiration, it tells us that if you aren't #1 you are nothing; or it may tell us that you just need to give your best and whatever happens is fate. Either way these are hollow motivators that cause us to fall short over time. But if we look to live and coach on the 'edge' daily with Christ and for His glory we will never be decimated when we aren't #1 at the end of the year, and we won't have to suffer through the agony of wondering why our 'best' wasn't good enough when we don't win all the time.

What do you put your hope in and what are your primary motivators? Do they match up with what God wants you to be motivated by?

III. LIVING FOR CHRIST - 'LIVING ON THE EDGE' (READ COLOSSIANS 3:23 & PHILIPPIANS 4:13)

Receiving Christ as Lord of your life is only the beginning. We must continue to follow Him as our coach by being rooted, strengthened and built up in the faith daily. Christ wants to guide us and help us with our daily struggles, but that means we must live on the edge daily with Christ and not be swayed by the world's motivations. **We *must see things through Jesus' eyes!***

How you can 'Live on the Edge' daily with Christ in the heat of competition:
1) Commit your life to Him and submit your will to Him.
2) Seek to learn from Christ, his life and his teachings.
3) Recognize the Holy Spirit's power in you and give God the glory!
4) Strive for excellence & Keep your eyes on Christ and study God's word.

COACHES CHALLENGE: Tell your players about the three sided coin and living/playing on the edge with Christ. Give them each a coin or penny to remind them daily of their commitment.

MEMORIZE: Galatians 2:20

I have been crucified with Christ and I no longer live, but Christ lives in me. The life I live in the body, I live by faith in the Son of God, who loved me and gave himself for me.
Answer Key: 1. draw 2. strength 3. Edge

WEEK 9

DIFFICULT PEOPLE...
DIFFICULT SITUATIONS

*"Your commitment to Jesus Christ will bring
out the best and the worst in others"*

READ: Matthew 7:1-5

I. THE DOUBLE-EDGED SWORD

Your commitment to the sport you coach and the passion that you bring to
your job each day can either draw people to you or drive them away. As you
grow closer to God in your Quest to become more like Christ in every way,
your_____ will both draw people to you and drive them from you. As
a leader, Jesus dealt with the same issue as he began to live out his
calling… People were either attracted to Him or repulsed by Him
depending on where their hearts were.

*Describe a situation that occurred where you felt that your commitment
to Christ caused a person or people to be drawn to you? How about the
converse…where you felt someone didn't want to be around you because
of your commitment to Christ? How does Jesus want us to handle both of
these situations?*

II. DIFFICULT PEOPLE IN DIFFICULT SITUATIONS! (JOHN 16:1-4)

God has chosen you to be a light that leads people to safety, just as a
lighthouse leads ships through dangerous waters. But God has also chosen
you to be a light in a dark, dark world. At times your light will be more than
a beacon of hope, it will be the light that exposes the emptiness, corruption

and sinful practices in people's lives. As a disciple of the Master Coach, you will experience both _____ and _____ due to your holiness. God will honor your daily commitment to Him by using you in mighty ways, but your mere presence may bring out the worst in others. But we should not be discouraged because Jesus warned us that this would happen and that we should not deviate from our _____. It is at these times, we need to remember that Christ prayed, "Father please forgive them, for they know not what they do."

How do you handle people that don't have any faith in God and rub you the wrong way? How does Jesus want us to handle it (find scripture examples)?

III. BRIDGING THE GAP WITH PRAYER (READ EPHESIANS 6:18)

We know that if we are not alert as coaches we can be caught off guard and lose a game or worse. When we find ourselves in difficult situations with others, we must stay alert and rely on Christ. We must handle every situation with prayer *(before, during and after)* if we hope to continue to grow and be a light in the darkness. We must pray on all occasions.

Why do you think prayer and 'standing in the gap' for others in prayer is such a big deal in God's eyes?

How you can 'Stand in the Gap' for Christ:
1) Pray in the Spirit on all occasions. (Before, during and after all situations)
2) Order your life around God's desires and teachings.
3) Don't isolate yourself from other people; it will inhibit your growth.
4) Pray for all believers and your enemies.

COACHES CHALLENGE: Think of someone that is not a believer and commit to praying for him or her on a daily basis. Ask God to lift the veil of unbelief that covers their eyes and soften their heart and fill them with the Holy Spirit...now tell that person you have been praying for them and stand in the gap!

MEMORIZE: John 15:17

This is my command: Love each other.

Answer Key: 1. holiness 2. blessings 3. difficulties 4. beliefs

GOD IS LOOKING FOR AN OBEDIENT COACH

"Being obedient allows God to do mighty things!"

READ: 1 John 2:3-6, Acts 20:24

I. YOUR OBEDIENCE ALLOWS GOD TO TAKE YOU TO ANOTHER LEVEL-SPIRITUALLY!

If we hope to be successful coaches we must have obedient assistant coaches and players. If our players practice _____ they will experience a level of play that they had only dreamed about previously. As we move along on our Quest to become more like Christ, God will ask us to make major adjustments and be obedient so that He can work through us. It is one thing to hear God, but it is another to obey what He commands us to do. If we truly want to become closer to God and get to a level of spiritual development that we had only dreamed about previously, we must _____ Him. As Christ said, "If you love me, you will obey what I command."

On your Quest to become more like Christ, list some things that God has asked you to do since you started these studies? Did you do them? Why or why not? What is God putting on your heart as you complete this study?

II. YOUR OBEDIENCE = YOUR LEVEL OF FAITH IN GOD (JOHN 14:15,24)

You can determine your players' level of _____ in your teachings by their level of _____ in difficult situations. As we live for the Master Coach, He is going to ask us to do some difficult things. How we react to those requests determines our level of faith in God. At times, obedience can even be painful, but just as our players must trust in us, we too, must trust in God's sovereignty, love and perfect will. Also, please remember how you feel when one of your players is disobedient. God also takes disobedience very seriously.

What keeps us from being obedient? How do you handle a disobedient player? How do you think God handles a disobedient believer?

 COACHES CHALLENGE: *Circle how you think God would rate your life in regard to Obedience to Him.*
Complete Disobedience 1 -2-3-4-5-6-7-8-9-10 Perfect Obedience

III. BIG THINGS START SMALL! (READ MATTHEW 25:21)

Many times we are disappointed with how slow God works or how small things start out. But we need not be discouraged, for as we show God that we can be faithful with a few things He will entrust us with much. If you don't see immediate results from a mentoring group or Bible study you're in, don't give up. If you remain obedient to what the Lord has asked He will ensure that what He has called you to do, He will follow through to completion.

How can you impact the coaching profession one coach at a time, one player at a time, and one person at a time? How can you influence your players both on and off the court/field spiritually? What is God calling you to do as you complete this study?

Benefits of Obedience:
1) It frees God to do mighty things
2) God will be with you…you will have greater fellowship with God (Jeremiah 7:23)
3) You will develop a strong foundation in Christ (Luke 6:46-49)
4) A new found depth of spiritual truths in Jesus' teachings (John 7:16-17)
5) God blesses those who are obedient (Deuteronomy 28:1-4)

MEMORIZE: James 2:20

Faith without works is dead.

Answer Key: 1. obedience 2. obey 3. faith 4. obedience

STUDY LEADER'S GUIDE

Dear Legacy Builder Group Leader of the Quest Bible Study,

Thank you for being obedient to your calling and welcome to the awesome and vital task of helping men and women in the most difficult profession in the world (coaching) see how God can use them to further His kingdom and leave a legacy. By accepting this call and challenge, you align yourself with the many followers of Jesus Christ who have listened to his call and agreed to commit to further His kingdom. As a Legacy Builder study leader, you may never completely know the impact you have for the kingdom until we all get to Heaven and are with the Father, but at that time it will be clear to all!

So I encourage you to be faithful with a little and to be patient with yourself and your group. It is not up to you to change people's hearts...that is God's job. It is your job to share the word of God and the biblical principles included in this study and God will do the rest. Remember, the Word of God never comes back void!

May you enjoy the weeks ahead, and may you enjoy God's blessing and favor as you serve Him faithfully with your study group. One of the greatest things Jesus did was to help people see how God can use them to further His kingdom in the everyday work of their lives. My prayer is that you too, will be blessed with Christ's presence and power as you strive to help others see the impact they can have, not only for their own eternity, but the eternity of their families, players and colleagues!

WHY A LEGACY BUILDER STUDY?

The Legacy Builder study series came from God and was developed to fulfill a need for coaches to have a relevant incremental Coaches Bible studies. I wrote the Legacy Builder series to have curriculum for our area coaches' bible studies for the Fellowship of Christian Athletes Coaches Ministry in Colorado. Several years ago, God brought a man into my life named Scotty Kessler. As a head football coach at the collegiate level, I brought Scotty in as a consultant to assess our football program and coaching staff. Through those meetings God used Scotty to teach me how to integrate Biblical principles into my coaching philosophy and program. My life was changed forever, as I finally had been given the knowledge and tools I needed for God to use me to minister to coaches and athletes through my coaching. As I went deeper in my relationship God, I found myself being called to the ministry with the yearning to tell others how coaching with Biblical principles changed my life! However, one of my biggest struggles as a Christian coach, was finding Bible studies that were relevant to my career as a coach. Surely, Jesus had something to say to a person that worked for a nickel an hour, 80 to 90 hours a week, was paid to win, and had hundreds of people that would listen to and believe anything I said! And besides, I needed to know what Jesus had to say about handling an angry parent or getting fired! Needless to say, I didn't find any studies in the book stores that dealt with those topics. After visiting with Johnny Square (chaplain for the Colorado State University football program) I decided to ask God to help me put on paper just a few of the principles I have been taught and that have allowed me to become close enough to God so that he may use me to leave a legacy for His kingdom through coaching.

YOUR LEGACY BUILDER GROUP

You are going to find an eager group of coaches in your weekly meetings. You are going to find that these studies cross all gender, race and sport. Coaches from all different levels and sports are going to enjoy great prayer time and fellowship while they learn. Every person wants to know how they can improve and every Christian coach wants to know how they can be a Christian, integrate their faith into their leadership and still strive to win and compete to God's glory! You are going to have a ball!

If you are a first time group leader or inexperienced group leader, you will enjoy the leadership guide and short lessons. Everything is based on the word of God and each lesson begins and ends with scripture. As Paul said, "My speech and my preaching not with persuasive words of human wisdom, but in demonstration of the Spirit and of power, that your faith should not be in the wisdom of men but in the power of God" (1 Corinthians 2: 4-5).

All you have to bring to the table each week is a willingness to serve God and others, the truth of God's word, and a total dependence upon God to do His work.

As you pray each week for those things and God's guidance, you will hear coaches share stories about what they have learned and how God is working in their lives. You will see lives transformed and you too will grow closer to God. Finally, as you finish the study with your group you will see the power of God move as your group members want to start their own Legacy Builder study groups with other coaches. And that is what leaving a legacy is all about! Praise God.

GROUND RULES FOR YOUR SMALL GROUP

To ensure that everyone in your group is on the same page, I would encourage you to lead the group in making 3 commitments:

1) Everyone agrees to and completes the Legacy Builder group covenant sheet located at the beginning of the study booklet. You don't need to collect the sheets but everyone should fill one out for their own level of commitment.
2) Everyone commits to spending time prior to meeting in preparation for the lesson. This is not a difficult task as the lessons are short.
3) Everyone commits to ask God to change their lives according to the Biblical truths presented.

THE STRUCTURE OF EACH LEGACY BUILDER LESSON

Each week, God leads coaches through a dynamic, life changing process through the lessons. Each lesson begins with a topic and scripture that ties to that specific topic or principle. There are fill in the blanks along with questions to facilitate thought and discussion. Finally the lesson, concludes with a "How to take Action" section which gives the coach practical tools and steps for how to implement the principle taught that day into their daily routines. But most importantly, each lesson concludes with scripture that is again relevant to the lesson's topic and the student is expected to memorize the verse or verses. Memorization is a key part of the weekly lesson as the Word of God is the sword of the Spirit.

WEEKLY LEADER NOTES FOR:
THE QUEST... "Coaching for Jesus In a Bottom-Line World"

Week 1 - THE QUEST
"Where you've been, where you are, & where you are going"

The Purpose of this lesson: Is to help the individual gain an understanding of three basic questions we all must answer (see below) and to recognize that God can use all your past experiences (good and bad) to further His kingdom. This lesson will also give the coach/parent a super biblical view of how to handle mistakes in and out of the athletic arena.

Major Focus of Lesson:
The 3 Questions we all must answer:
1)Where did I come from?
2)Why am I here?
3)Where am I going?

Three Things to do when you or your players make a mistake:
1)Admit it.
2)Fix it.
3) Forget it & Don't Repeat it.

THE LESSON
"Putting Sand in their Sandals"
Scripture Reference notes for Week 1

Romans 12:2

Tips: Prior to asking someone to read Romans 12:2 or any other scriptures during the lesson it is important for the facilitator to "put sand in your group members sandals". In other words it is imperative that you get them to mentally understand the context of the scripture that is about to be read. It is the facilitator's job to give a brief background of who wrote the text, to whom the text was written, what was happening in the culture at the time the text was written and why was it written. This is not difficult if the facilitator possesses a study Bible that gives such information at the beginning of each book. This is also easily accomplished by reading the text prior to and following the section we will be discussing.

For Example: "The book of Romans is a letter written by Paul the apostle to the Christian church in Rome. We must remember how Rome was such an important and pivotal city at this time in history. The purpose of this letter was to prepare the Christian church for Paul's visit to Rome and more importantly to present the basic gospel or plan of salvation to a church that had not received the teaching of an apostle before. Paul looked forward to visiting Rome very much. He also knew that they needed to hear sound doctrine in regard to what Christianity is and how it is to be lived. Lastly, the section we are about to read deals with helping the Christian learn how to live a transformed life in Jesus Christ. Now let's hear what God's servant Paul had to say..."

Lesson Tips for Week 1
Tips for Part 1 "Quest":
*Discuss the three questions listed and how important it is as Christians that we can answers these succinctly and clearly.

*Next move into the question that if the apostle Paul were coaching you what would it mean to be 'transformed by the renewing of your mind?"

*Talk about how disciplined action comes from disciplined thoughts. It all starts with our heart and thought process.

Tips for Part 2 "The Past":
*This may be a sensitive part of some people's lives as they look at their past. Be sure to focus on the question and not people's past issues. Remind them that God is about using all things for good and the enemy is about

tearing things apart.

*Focus in on why people don't want to share their past and how that is not of God and the enemy is trying to use fear to keep us from letting God use us.

Tips for Part 3 "The Present":

*Read Philippians 2:13 first. Remind them that it is our job to ask for help and God's job to work in us and help us live our lives on a daily basis the way Christ would.

*Emphasize that we cannot live the great life God has in store for us if we hold on to past sins and mistakes. If we want to embark on a great journey of life with Christ we must trust in the fact that our sins are forgiven and they are at the bottom of the ocean!

The enemy is about making us feel that we are too horrible to be loved and forgiven by God and nothing can be further from the truth. We need only to cling to Jesus Christ and ask for forgiveness. God uses everyone!

*Focus on why God uses fallen people to further his kingdom...He needs people who are not perfect to speak into the lives of struggling like people. People want to hear from others who have been wounded and have come through it or are working on it.

How to Take Action:

*The key to success in life is determined by our ability to learn from our mistakes. If we do not try and fail we will not progress. Thomas Edison, the great inventor viewed his failures as "one less incorrect way" not to do something on his way to discover success.

*Free yourself up and your players to not be afraid to fail by asking yourself and your players/kids to do only 3 things that Jesus taught..Admit it, fix it and don't repeat it. Show how that parallels confession, repentance and living a transformed life.

*Tell the coaches that next week you will be asking them if they asked God to use them. If they practiced the 3 things you do when you make a mistake and could they discuss how God went ahead of them last week.

*Read Memory Verse and remind them that the first step of their journey or Quest is to seek out the good works that God has prepared for them in advance through prayer. Lastly, close in Prayer as the facilitator.

Week 2 - THE CLIMB… "Stepping Stones or Spiritual Landmarks"
The Purpose of this lesson: Is three fold: One, we want to help the individual recognize that God has been in control of their lives since day one. Secondly, we will help the individual learn how to put God's will in their lives first as they deal with career decisions as well as daily decisions. Lastly, we will help the individual take a look at their past and put together a 'Spiritual landmark' list to help them see how God has worked in their lives and how that can help them as they want to make Godly decisions in the future.

Major Focus of Lesson:
*Developing their Spiritual Landmark List and seeing how God has worked and is working in their lives.

***How to make Tough Decisions** - How to choose between good and better.

THE LESSON
"Putting Sand in their Sandals"
Scripture Reference notes for Week 2
Romans 8:28-33
Tips: Prior to asking someone to read Romans 8:28-33 or any other scriptures during the lesson it is important for the facilitator to "put sand in your group members sandals". In other words it is imperative that you get them to mentally understand the context of the scripture that is about to be read. It is the facilitator's job to give a brief background of who wrote the text, to whom the text was written, what was happening in the culture at the time the text was written and why was it written. This is not difficult if the facilitator possesses a study Bible that gives such information at the beginning of each book. This is also easily accomplished by reading the text prior to and following the section we will be discussing.
For Example: "The book of Romans is a letter written by Paul the apostle to the Christian church in Rome. We must remember how Rome was such an important and pivotal city at this time in history. The purpose of this letter was to prepare the Christian church for Paul's visit to Rome and more importantly to present the basic gospel or plan of salvation to a church that had not received the teaching of an apostle before. Paul looked forward to visiting Rome very much. He also knew that they needed to hear sound doctrine in regard to what Christianity is and how it is to be lived. Lastly,

the section we are about to read deals with helping the Christian learn how to live a transformed life in Jesus Christ. Now let's hear what God's servant Paul had to say…"

Lesson Tips for Week 2
Tips for Part 1 "Predestined":
*Discuss how God had chosen them long before they were born for His glory.

*Next move into discussion about a situation where they knew God was involved as they look back at it now?"

*Finish with the fact that we need to have the goal of seeing all things past and present from God's viewpoint.

Tips for Part 2 "My Will vs. God's Will":
*Read Matthew 6:9-11 and remind them that it is God's will that needs to be accomplished not ours.

*Remind them that if we want to make God pleasing decisions we must put God's will first in the process of prayer.

*Have fun discussing ideas about how people make their decisions between good and better and putting God's will first and what the benefits were.

Tips for Part 3 "Spiritual landmarks":
*Even though we cannot predict what God will do in our lives, we would like to follow His plan for our lives when we have decisions to make. By looking at a list of the spiritual landmarks in our lives of where God was at work, we can use that as sort of a scouting report to help us in our future decisions.

*Make sure everyone understands how to make a spiritual landmark list. Just have them go back as far as they can remember and list major events, directions and decisions that were made in their lives and list them in chronological order. Then look at them from an overview just as God would.

How to Take Action (How to make tough decisions):
*The key to making tough decisions and staying in God's will is to pray and seek His will first.

*Focus on Point 2 and the spiritual landmark list again.

*Lastly if they are waiting on the Lord for an answer or guidance point out that waiting means to tarry or to be doing something while you are waiting, i.e., seeking God with all your heart, mind and soul!

*Read Memory Verse and remind them that they are predestined by God and chosen and that God is there to help us with all our decisions and that we must be patient. Lastly, close in Prayer as the facilitator.

WEEK 3 - BE TO DO...NOT DO TO BE!
"God wants a changed heart...not blind obedience"

The Purpose of this lesson: Is to help the individual (coach or athlete) realize that a life that is transformed by Jesus Christ is not a life of busyness. We cannot 'work' ourselves into a closer relationship with God. We must be motivated by the heart to seek the King. A transformed life is not one that sees how many Bible studies we can go to or how many times we can go to church. Following this lesson the individual will understand that God is looking for an authentic faith walk that isn't measured by spiritual activities but by a heart that integrates Jesus Christ into all things.

Major Focus of Lesson:
How can we learn to be still and know God? What does a transformed life look like? We must learn to live our lives at an 80% capacity with 20% available for God to lead us, instead of constantly operating at 120% capacity. We can't do this without the help of the Holy Spirit.

THE LESSON
"Putting Sand in their Sandals"
Scripture Reference notes for Week 3

Tips: Prior to asking someone to read 1 Corinthians 15:7-10 or the Luke passage or any other scriptures during the lesson it is important for the facilitator to "put sand in your group members sandals". In other words it is imperative that you get them to mentally understand the context of the scripture that is about to be read. It is the facilitator's job to give a brief background of who wrote the text, to whom the text was written, what was happening in the culture at the time the text was written and why was it written. This is not difficult if the facilitator possesses a study Bible that gives such information at the beginning of each book. This is also easily accomplished by reading the text prior to and following the section we will be discussing.

For Example: "The book of Romans is a letter written by Paul the apostle to the Christian church in Rome. We must remember how Rome was such an important and pivotal city at this time in history. The purpose of this letter was to prepare the Christian church for Paul's visit to Rome and more importantly to present the basic gospel or plan of salvation to a church that had not received the teaching of an apostle before. Paul looked forward to visiting Rome very much. He also knew that they needed to hear sound doctrine in regard to what Christianity is and how it is to be lived. Lastly, the section we are about to read deals with helping the Christian learn how to live a transformed life in Jesus Christ. Now let's hear what God's servant Paul had to say…"

Lesson Tips for Week 3
Tips for Part 1 "The Grinder":
*Discuss how as coaches it is engraved upon us to outwork others and how this trait is not helpful in trying to grow closer to God.
*In fact, the harder we work to get closer to God the less we understand the type of relationship our Father is looking for with us.
*Talk about how God is looking for our hearts and time…not busy work and us putting checks in our check boxes.

Tips for Part 2 "Be Transformed - integrate Jesus into everything!"
*Focus on the fact that a transformed life in Jesus Christ means that it is your character or what God has etched upon your heart.
*Remind them that we all need to be 'people oriented and not task oriented'.

Tips for Part 3 "Resting in God…Hard Work":
*Read Luke 10: 38-42 first. Ask them to discuss whether they are a Martha personality (very task oriented) or a Mary personality (God perspective focused).

How to Take Action (How to maintain consistency between your heart and your actions):
*Follow the numbered examples and focus on point #4.
*Tell the coaches that next week you will be asking them if they have simplified their activity down to 80% or 90% instead of 120% and how that affected their relationship with God.
*Read Memory Verse and remind them that the second step on their Quest for living a transformed life in Jesus Christ is to be like Mary and not a Martha. Simplify their lives and have a heart for Christ.
Lastly, close in Prayer as the facilitator.

WEEK 4 - MATURITY THROUGH ADVERSITY...
"Everyone wants to go to heaven but no one wants to die"

The Purpose of this lesson: Is to help the individual understand the Biblical principle that God is growing and developing our faith through adversity and difficult situations He is not trying to make our lives and our Christian walk a miserable one.

Major Focus of Lesson:
*Gain an understanding that adversity can become a distraction if we aren't careful and see things from God's perspective.
*Also, that if we continue to just go with our gut instincts and not to God first in difficult situations we will be distracted and disjointed in our lives.

THE LESSON
"Putting Sand in their Sandals"
Scripture Reference notes for Week 4
James 1:1-8
Tips: Prior to asking someone to read James 1:1-8 or any other scriptures during the lesson it is important for the facilitator to "put sand in your group members sandals". In other words it is imperative that you get them to mentally understand the context of the scripture that is about to be read. It is the facilitator's job to give a brief background of who wrote the text, to whom the text was written, what was happening in the culture at the time the text was written and why was it written. This is not difficult if the facilitator possesses a study Bible that gives such information at the beginning of each book. This is also easily accomplished by reading the text prior to and following the section we will be discussing.
For Example: "The book of Romans is a letter written by Paul the apostle to the Christian church in Rome. We must remember how Rome was such an important and pivotal city at this time in history. The purpose of this letter was to prepare the Christian church for Paul's visit to Rome and more importantly to present the basic gospel or plan of salvation to a church that had not received the teaching of an apostle before. Paul looked forward to visiting Rome very much. He also knew that they needed to hear sound doctrine in regard to what Christianity is and how it is to be lived. Lastly, the section we are about to read deals with helping the Christian learn how to live a transformed life in Jesus Christ. Now let's hear what God's servant Paul had to say..."

Lesson Tips for Week 4
Tips for Part 1 "No Pain...No Gain":
*Discuss how James was a real guy that understood the difficulties in life and how to approach them.

*Next talk about how maturity comes through adversity. Use the analogy of learning from defeats and tough losses.

*Reinforce that God is about developing spiritual warriors not spoiled people with no adversity in their lives.

Tips for Part 2 "Distraction vs Opportunity":
*Read 2 Corinthians and reiterate the fact that we must have faith that God is working for the good (Rom. 8:28) in all things. Especially when adversity hits.

*Reinforce that we must see our trials as opportunities for growth otherwise we will not persevere.

*Focus on the extra point for a few minutes and see how pain can be a good thing that focuses our attention on what really needs to have our full attention.

Tips for Part 3 "God's Way or My Way":
*Many times we are too impatient to wait for God and we just go with our gut instincts. This isn't all bad, but we must always put God first and His perspective if we hope to endure adversity.

*See Coaches Challenge and discuss thoroughly. As Coaches deal with many conflicts.

How to Take Action (How to see trials as growing points not breaking points):
*Remind them that Satan wants us to be focused on the problem so that we can't see God clearly.

*Point #2 stresses using your experiences to help others...we like to say that God knows people won't trust anyone without a limp. In other words, people want help from people who have been in their situation and have learned from it.

*Read Memory Verse and remind them that the journey is all about God developing Christ-like characteristics in us. This cannot be accomplished without adversity. . Lastly, close in Prayer as the facilitator and ask God to give them the courage and vision to stand firm in their faith and to live by faith and not by sight.

WEEK 5 - SELF-SERVING LEADER TO SERVANT-LEADER...
"With God it's all about people not productivity!"

The Purpose of this lesson: Is to help leaders understand that God is not about worldly success or wins and losses when He measures us. God is about people and how you serve them as a coach and leader.
This lesson will teach leaders the Biblical principle of trusting that God has your back, and that He wants you to be a servant leader so that the people you lead will be the same type of leaders.

Major Focus of Lesson:
The 3 major areas of focus start with having a Biblical viewpoint rather than a world viewpoint. Next, we focus on people not productivity. We are about relationships. Lastly, in order to die to ourselves and serve others we need to have tools for our toolboxes or helpers to keep us on the track of being a servant leader.

THE LESSON
"Putting Sand in their Sandals"
Scripture Reference notes for Week 5
Matthew 20:25-28
Tips: Prior to asking someone to read Matthew 20:25-28 or any other scriptures during the lesson it is important for the facilitator to "put sand in your group members sandals". In other words it is imperative that you get them to mentally understand the context of the scripture that is about to be read. It is the facilitator's job to give a brief background of who wrote the text, to whom the text was written, what was happening in the culture at the time the text was written and why was it written. This is not difficult if the facilitator possesses a study Bible that gives such information at the beginning of each book. This is also easily accomplished by reading the text prior to and following the section we will be discussing.
For Example: "The book of Romans is a letter written by Paul the apostle to the Christian church in Rome. We must remember how Rome was such an important and pivotal city at this time in history. The purpose of this letter was to prepare the Christian church for Paul's visit to Rome and more importantly to present the basic gospel or plan of salvation to a church that had not received the teaching of an apostle before. Paul looked forward to visiting Rome very much. He also knew that they needed to hear sound doctrine in regard to what Christianity is and how it is to be lived. Lastly,

the section we are about to read deals with helping the Christian learn how to live a transformed life in Jesus Christ. Now let's hear what God's servant Paul had to say..."

Lesson Tips for Week 5
Tips for Part 1 "World Thinking vs. Biblical Truths":
*Lead by stating that the #1 problem we face today is that we are constantly forced to see things from the world's viewpoint. As Christians that cannot be the case, we must see all things from God's perspective. Especially, when it comes to serving others as opposed to putting ourselves first.

*As you discuss how to coach from a Biblical viewpoint focus in on the fact that they are coaching to further God's kingdom through sport by developing servant leaders and teaching kids life-lessons through sport and helping them not only win on the field but more importantly in life, specifically eternal life!

Tips for Part 2 "Be Ruthless with your time not with people!":
*This may be a difficult proposition for many as we think we are always short on time. Here we need to reinforce that our time is very valuable, but people are even more valuable in God's economy.

*Spend time on having people take an inventory on who is getting 'the best parts or meat' of their time.

Tips for Part 3 "Die to yourself and live for Christ":
*Read Romans 6:11-14 and reiterate that being a servant leader is a lifestyle not just a convenience. Remind them that what they are doing is hugely significant in the spiritual realm as they may not only help Christians but they may be the only Bible some people ever read!

How to Take Action (A Servant Leader's Toolbox):
*You will now walk them through each one of the tools listed and help them to understand what each looks like. For example, a mission statement and definition of success that is only a paragraph long.

*Read Memory Verse and remind them that Jesus Christ was the ultimate servant leader and they can be too if they are focused on God's viewpoint and they don't care what the world thinks. Lastly, ASK someone to close in Prayer as the facilitator.

WEEK 6 - BATTLING THE ENEMY...
"Winning spiritual battles and freeing yourself in Jesus Christ"

The Purpose of this lesson: Is to give the individual a basic understanding of spiritual warfare and a Biblical prayer plan for how they can help themselves and others gain freedom in Christ through His crucifixion, death and resurrection and grace.

Major Focus of Lesson:
*Give people a basic understanding of how the enemy uses sin to keep us in bondage and keep us from being/living freely in Christ.
*Give people a Biblically based prayer plan of the 6 R's of forgiveness and freedom.

THE LESSON and SCRIPTURE REFERENCE
"Putting Sand in their Sandals"
Scripture Reference notes for Week 6
Peter 5:7-9 and Hebrews 12:6-11
Tips: Prior to asking someone to read Peter 5:7-9 and Hebrews 12:6-11 or any other scriptures during the lesson it is important for the facilitator to "put sand in your group members sandals". In other words it is imperative that you get them to mentally understand the context of the scripture that is about to be read. It is the facilitator's job to give a brief background of who wrote the text, to whom the text was written, what was happening in the culture at the time the text was written and why was it written. This is not difficult if the facilitator possesses a study Bible that gives such information at the beginning of each book. This is also easily accomplished by reading the text prior to and following the section we will be discussing. For Example: "The book of Romans is a letter written by Paul the apostle to the Christian church in Rome. We must remember how Rome was such an important and pivotal city at this time in history. The purpose of this letter was to prepare the Christian church for Paul's visit to Rome and more importantly to present the basic gospel or plan of salvation to a church that had not received the teaching of an apostle before. Paul looked forward to visiting Rome very much. He also knew that they needed to hear sound doctrine in regard to what Christianity is and how it is to be lived. Lastly, the section we are about to read deals with helping the Christian learn how to live a transformed life in Jesus Christ. Now let's hear what God's servant Paul had to say..."

Lesson Tips for Week 6
Tips for Part 1 "Whatever doesn't kill you makes you stronger":
*In this section we are looking to give the leader an understanding of discipline and why and how God uses it.
*It is important to focus on the fact that discipline is a good thing when seen from the parent's (God's) viewpoint.
*See the extra point and note that God is about disciplining us to draw us closer to Himself, while Satan attacks us to put distance between us and God.

Tips for Part 2 "The Battle in the Courtroom of God":
*The purpose of this section is to paint a picture for the individual as to how unconfessed sin affects our relationship with God and also how Satan tries to make us feel guilty about things we have done in the past in hopes of making us think/feel that we are not worthy of being a Christian.
*It is important that you as the facilitator tell this in story form and make everyone understand that God is a loving judge who wants to free us and all we need to do is confess our sins to Jesus and we are a cleansed, the penalty has been paid by Jesus Christ and Satan has no hold on us.
 Tips for Part 3 "The 6 R's of Forgiveness and Freedom in Jesus Christ":
*Reinforce that this is not some magic formula. We are talking about prayer, confession, repentance, forgiveness and freedom in Christ based upon the Bible and Jesus' teachings.
*Emphasize that by praying the 6 R's we are claiming victory over death and Satan through the name of Jesus Christ, the Word of God and the power of Prayer!
*I encourage you to have a different person read each scripture reference for each of the R's so they see the Biblical basis for each.

How to Take Action:
*The How to Take Action in this lesson is by beginning to go to the courtroom of God each day willingly and by praying the 6 R's with authority. There is much more to this lesson however, our purpose is only to expose the individuals with basic battle tactics as we war against the rulers of this dark world (Eph. 6:12).
*Read Memory Verse and remind them that God is revealing many things to them along their Quest to be like Jesus Christ. Jesus was a warrior that knew how to battle and so must they. Lastly, close in Prayer as the facilitator.

WEEK 7 - EASY TO PLEASE BUT HARD TO SATISFY...

"God will put you in tough situations to show you how to serve Him"
The Purpose of this lesson: Is to help the coach understand that God is the
Master Coach who is easy to please but always wants us to strive for more.
We also want the coach to understand that he/she can be a coach that
possesses those same traits and that through Jesus Christ and His word;
God prepares us for pressure situations.

Major Focus of Lesson:

*As a coach or a player on God's team we really only control 2 things: our
attitude and our effort. Effort, meaning that we are striving to be like Jesus
Christ each day.
*God has prepared us for pressure situations and He will not test us
beyond what we can bear with His help (1 Corinthians 10:13).
*How you can thrive in pressure situations as a coach and a Christian.

THE LESSON and SCRIPTURE REFERENCE
"Putting Sand in their Sandals"

Scripture Reference notes for Week 7
2 Timothy 2:1-7
Tips: Prior to asking someone to read 2 Timothy 2:1-7 or any other
scriptures during the lesson it is important for the facilitator to "put sand in
your group members sandals". In other words it is imperative that you get
them to mentally understand the context of the scripture that is about to be
read. It is the facilitator's job to give a brief background of who wrote the
text, to whom the text was written, what was happening in the culture at
the time the text was written and why was it written. This is not difficult if
the facilitator possesses a study Bible that gives such information at the
beginning of each book. This is also easily accomplished by reading the text
prior to and following the section we will be discussing.
For Example: "The book of Romans is a letter written by Paul the apostle to
the Christian church in Rome. We must remember how Rome was such an
important and pivotal city at this time in history. The purpose of this letter
was to prepare the Christian church for Paul's visit to Rome and more
importantly to present the basic gospel or plan of salvation to a church that
had not received the teaching of an apostle before. Paul looked forward to
visiting Rome very much. He also knew that they needed to hear sound
doctrine in regard to what Christianity is and how it is to be lived. Lastly,
the section we are about to read deals with helping the Christian learn how

to live a transformed life in Jesus Christ. Now let's hear what God's servant
Paul had to say…"

Lesson Tips for Week 7
Tips for Part 1 "Preparing for Adversity":
*Discuss the Scripture from 2 Timothy and Paul's analogies to a soldier and
a soldier's viewpoint toward adversity. The Marines say, "Adapt, adjust and
overcome!"
*Next focus on the fact that they need to share with their players that they
only control 2 things, Attitude and Effort. See how that takes pressure off of
their players and watch them play better!

Tips for Part 2 "The Pressure Cooker":
*Read 1 Corinthians 10:12-13 and make sure they understand that whatever
they are going through is not something no one else has ever gone through
and that they will not be tested past what they can handle "with God's
Help". If we try to overcome temptation on our own we will most likely fail.
*I usually tell a story here about what real pressure is, i.e., you have 3
children who haven't eaten for 3 days and the welfare check did not come
in the mail…what do you do? Or your little sister needs her medicine and if
you give her the wrong dose she could die and … you can't read! Now that
is pressure, not some basketball or football game. We must keep
perspective on what pressure really is.

Tips for Part 3 "God is the Perfect Coach…":
*Focus in on what it means to be a coach that is easy to please and hard to
satisfy. That means that the coach is positive and says, "That was great
you're getting it…now let's see if you can do this!"
*That is the type of God we serve and the group must be reminded of that
and they must coach like that!

How to Take Action (How you can thrive under pressure):
*Remind them that they can only control their attitude and their effort so
quit worrying about all the things you can't control.
* It always comes back to being disciplined and seeking God with all your
heart, mind and soul daily.
*Remind them to remain confident in the promises of God's word and to
approach difficult situations with God not without Him.
*Read Memory Verse and remind them to take heart, be confident, have

hope, Jesus knew all this and dealt with it so that we have peace in pressure situations. Lastly, Ask someone to close in Prayer.

WEEK 8 - COACHING & LIVING 'ON THE EDGE'
"Gaining the edge of living daily with Jesus Christ...the door to being in the zone!"

The Purpose of this lesson: Is to give the individual a different perspective on what motivates us as competitors and Christians and that God does not want weak Christian competitors, he wants warriors that understand how to bridal the power he gives us, just as Jesus Christ did.

Major Focus of Lesson:
*In our Quest to become like Jesus Christ we must realize that he was a competitor for His father's kingdom and a warrior that was not driven by comparison or just doing his best. He was motivated to be the best He could possibly be based upon the gifts His father had given Him. God wants us to focus on living on the edge with Christ as a warrior and competitor in His kingdom while we're in the world.

THE LESSON and SCRIPTURE REFERENCE
"Putting Sand in their Sandals"
Scripture Reference notes for Week 8
Colossians 2:6-15 and Matthew 5:5
Tips: Prior to asking someone to read Colossians 2:6-15 and Matthew 5:5 or any other scriptures during the lesson it is important for the facilitator to "put sand in your group members sandals". In other words it is imperative that you get them to mentally understand the context of the scripture that is about to be read. It is the facilitator's job to give a brief background of who wrote the text, to whom the text was written, what was happening in the culture at the time the text was written and why was it written. This is not difficult if the facilitator possesses a study Bible that gives such information at the beginning of each book. This is also easily accomplished by reading the text prior to and following the section we will be discussing. For Example: "The book of Romans is a letter written by Paul the apostle to the Christian church in Rome. We must remember how Rome was such an important and pivotal city at this time in history. The purpose of this letter was to prepare the Christian church for Paul's visit to Rome and more importantly to present the basic gospel or plan of salvation to a church that

had not received the teaching of an apostle before. Paul looked forward to visiting Rome very much. He also knew that they needed to hear sound doctrine in regard to what Christianity is and how it is to be lived. Lastly, the section we are about to read deals with helping the Christian learn how to live a transformed life in Jesus Christ. Now let's hear what God's servant Paul had to say…"

Lesson Tips for Week 8
Tips for Part 1 "Submitting to Christ for strength":

*We must change our view of Jesus Christ. Here we like to discuss that Jesus was a construction/carpenter worker for most of his life and they had no power tools! We must realize that Jesus was not the weak, pale, frail man that we see in the paintings. I personally believe he may have had very dark skin and tan, 6'3" 210lbs with a 34" vertical and ran a 4.5 second 40 yard dash!

*Next we really focus on the definition of weak vs. meek. We utilize the meanings that weak is to be without power and meek is bridled power. We want to be meek.

*Reemphasize that it takes more strength to be meek and to know when to yield power than to just bully people.

Tips for Part 2 "The Three sided Coin… Another Way to Coach":

*This is a complete paradigm shift from the coaching culture and as the facilitator you need to tell them so. We discuss that players are motivated currently two ways: One, by being compared to others, "I am better than so and so or we are the best because we beat them." Two, there is a camp that just tells competitors to do their best and the outcome is up to the sport gods. The problem with this style of motivation is that if I am a competitor my best may not be good enough to win, then what? However, there is a third form of motivation (the edge) which focuses on what Jesus wants us to focus on and that is doing the best with what we have and striving to be the best we can be each time we compete. The measuring stick is mastery of skill or with God it is trying to be like Jesus Christ. We know we will fail at times but we will never tire from being compared to others or just "doing our best" until we get defeated so much we give up.

*Read the Extra Point and ask them what the quote means to them.

Tips for Part 3 "Living for Christ - Living on the Edge":

*Read Colossians 3:23 and Philippians 4:13 first. Remind them that we are to live for the Lord and not for men and that we draw the strength to do that from Christ Jesus!

How to Take Action:
*Tell them to see the challenge and give them an FCA coin so that every time they reach into their pocket they will feel the coin and remember to compete, coach and live on the edge with the power of Jesus Christ!
*Read Memory Verse and remind them that they are on a journey and that their Quest to be more like Jesus Christ means that they need to apply what they learned this week and then ask someone to close in Prayer as the facilitator.

WEEK 9 - DIFFICULT PEOPLE IN DIFFICULT SITUATIONS
"Your reverence for God will bring out the worst and the best in others"

The Purpose of this lesson: Is to encourage the coach or leader as they grow in their faith and to help them as their holiness becomes more apparent in their lives. Just as Jesus Christ was loved by many and hated by others, we too must be prepared for either situation and how we handle the latter as Christians is paramount and that is the purpose of this lesson

Major Focus of Lesson: LOVE
*Realizing that our reverence for God can bring out the best and the worst in others.
*How to handle people that don't like who you are in Christ.
*How to pray in difficult situations, how to pray for others and why that is so important in God's economy.

THE LESSON and SCRIPTURE REFERENCE
"Putting Sand in their Sandals"
Scripture Reference notes for Week 9
John 15:17-26 and John 16:1-4
Tips: Prior to asking someone to read John 15:17-26 and John 16:1-4 or any other scriptures during the lesson it is important for the facilitator to "put sand in your group members sandals". In other words it is imperative that you get them to mentally understand the context of the scripture that is about to be read. It is the facilitator's job to give a brief background of who wrote the text, to whom the text was written, what was happening in the

culture at the time the text was written and why was it written. This is not difficult if the facilitator possesses a study Bible that gives such information at the beginning of each book. This is also easily accomplished by reading the text prior to and following the section we will be discussing.

For Example: "The book of Romans is a letter written by Paul the apostle to the Christian church in Rome. We must remember how Rome was such an important and pivotal city at this time in history. The purpose of this letter was to prepare the Christian church for Paul's visit to Rome and more importantly to present the basic gospel or plan of salvation to a church that had not received the teaching of an apostle before. Paul looked forward to visiting Rome very much. He also knew that they needed to hear sound doctrine in regard to what Christianity is and how it is to be lived. Lastly, the section we are about to read deals with helping the Christian learn how to live a transformed life in Jesus Christ. Now let's hear what God's servant Paul had to say…"

Lesson Tips for Week 9
Tips for Part 1 "The Double-Edged Sword":
*The Scriptures are huge in the beginning of this lesson. Here the facilitator must reinforce the fact that Jesus knew believers would be persecuted and he prepared us for it! And the reason he prepared us is written in John 16:1, so we would not go astray! That is big!
*Spend some time discussing how Jesus handled difficult situations with people that didn't like who he was.
Tips for Part 2 "Difficult People in Difficult Situations":
*Read John 16:1-4 again and talk about the question dealing with non-believers or as we like to call them "Pre-Christians"!
*Have them share the scriptural examples they were supposed to find.
Tips for Part 3 "Bridging the Gap with Prayer":
*Read Ephesians 6:18 first. Tell them that when Paul writes about praying for the saints, that means all believers in Jesus Christ. Next spend time discussing what Spirit led prayer is and why do we need to do it all the time?
*When discussing why standing in the gap for someone is such a big deal in God's eyes, share that God is looking for people to pray on others behalf so He can act! (see old testament)

How to Take Action (How you can stand in the gap for Christ):
*It is important that we are praying for believers constantly, however it is

also very important that we pray for those who are not yet believers and these may even be our enemies.

*State how it is important that we pray for God to change people's hearts, that the Holy Spirit would hover over them continuously and that the veil of unbelief would be lifted from their eyes. This is specific prayer that empowers group members to be in very focused prayer for others.

*Read Memory Verse and let them know that you are proud of their progress and that you are inspired by the lives they are living. Also, remind them that the Christian life here on earth is a constant battle, but they are warriors and Jesus Christ is looking for them to further His kingdom!

Lastly, tell them it is still all about loving others and ask someone to close in Prayer as the facilitator.

WEEK 10 - GOD CAN & WILL USE AN OBEDIENT COACH
"Being obedient brings great adventure & allows God to do mighty things"

The Purpose of this lesson: Is to help the individual ask God what He wants to do with their life, discover what that calling is, and being obedient to that calling. We will also show the individual how one person or one coach can make a huge difference in hundreds of lives, change a culture for Christ and further God's kingdom through sport.

Major Focus of Lesson:
*Becoming more like Christ means being obedient.
*Being obedient allows God to do mighty things here on earth!
*Our level of obedience is equal to our level of Faith in God.
*Be patient…God works through one person at a time and through multiplication…don't get discouraged.

THE LESSON and SCRIPTURE REFERENCE
"Putting Sand in their Sandals"
Scripture Reference notes for Week 10
1 John 2:3-6 and Acts 20:24
Tips: Prior to asking someone to read 1 John 2:3-6 and Acts 20:24 or any other scriptures during the lesson it is important for the facilitator to "put sand in your group members sandals". In other words it is imperative that you get them to mentally understand the context of the scripture that is about to be read. It is the facilitator's job to give a brief background of who

wrote the text, to whom the text was written, what was happening in the culture at the time the text was written and why was it written. This is not difficult if the facilitator possesses a study Bible that gives such information at the beginning of each book. This is also easily accomplished by reading the text prior to and following the section we will be discussing.

For Example: "The book of Romans is a letter written by Paul the apostle to the Christian church in Rome. We must remember how Rome was such an important and pivotal city at this time in history. The purpose of this letter was to prepare the Christian church for Paul's visit to Rome and more importantly to present the basic gospel or plan of salvation to a church that had not received the teaching of an apostle before. Paul looked forward to visiting Rome very much. He also knew that they needed to hear sound doctrine in regard to what Christianity is and how it is to be lived. Lastly, the section we are about to read deals with helping the Christian learn how to live a transformed life in Jesus Christ. Now let's hear what God's servant Paul had to say…"

Lesson Tips for Week 10
Tips for Part 1 "Your obedience allows God to take you to another level spiritually!":
*Ask them why they started this study in the first place. If they are on a Quest to be more like Jesus Christ and grow closer to God, courage and obedience are the culminating steps!
*Spend quite a bit of time letting each person share what God has asked him or her to do throughout the weeks of this study.
Tips for Part 2 "Your Obedience = Your level of faith in God":
*Read John 14:15,24 and discuss how straight forward this topic is with Jesus. Remind them that all of this is still about love…loving others as yourself and loving God with all you heart, mind and soul.
If we truly love God we will obey Him. If we do not we won't. If we trust God we will obey Him.
*Next spend some time talking about how as coaches we deal with disobedient players and how God (the perfect Coach) deals with disobedient Christians.
*Have people share where they were on the Challenge segment for Perfect Obedience in God's eyes.

Tips for Part 3 "Big things start small!":
*Read Matthew 25:21 first and remind the group that God rarely starts things on a grand scale throughout the history of scripture. God usually

begins small and then it grows to a larger scale from there. It is our job to be faithful with a little and let God take care of the rest! But we must be obedient!

*Discuss ways they can influence their players on the court/field spiritually, i.e., spiritual themes like perseverance, peace, patience etc. Modeling servant leadership, team bible studies or Winning God's Way groups. You can place Greek slogans for a yearly theme on t-shirts. Have them share ideas.

*Have people share what they believe God is asking them to do now that they have completed this study. They could start their own Legacy Builder group, mentor athletes or disciple another coach, be a part of the final study in the Legacy Builder study series, The Master Playbook for Biblical Discipleship.

How to Take Action (Benefits of Obedience):
*See the Extra Point and remind them that God is not about wins and losses or the number of people you lead to Christ, He is about growing you closer to Him in relationship and you being obedient and faithful to Him. He is about what type of Legacy you will leave when you go to heaven.
*Have everyone read one of the scriptures that coincide with the 5 benefits of obedience.

*Read Memory Verse and remind them to see you afterward to let you know what they are planning to do next and remember for yourself as the facilitator to bless them and encourage them and let them know you will be praying for them to follow and obey God's will. Lastly, close in Prayer and remember the Quest to be like Christ will never end until we leave this world. Praise God!

For the Group Leader/Legacy Builder

*Thank you again for taking time to learn, live and lead for Jesus Christ and his kingdom. You are leaving an awesome Legacy and fulfilling the great commission. May God bless you, show you favor and establish the work of your hands. (Psalm 90:17)

We would love to hear stories of your Legacy Builder group please email us at **Rolson@fca.org or**
Visit our website www.coachesministry.com

For more information on the Legacy Builder Sport Discipleship Series go to
www.coachesministry.com or www.crosstraining publishing.com